$\mathcal{A}$DDRESS BOOK

A directory of flowers and friends

INDEX

First published in 1996 by Lorenz Books

© Anness Publishing Limited 1996

Lorenz Books is an imprint of Anness Publishing Limited
Boundary Row Studios
1 Boundary Row
London SE1 8HP

ISBN 1 85967 131 4

Distributed in Canada by Book Express, an imprint of
Raincoast Books Distribution Limited

A CIP catalogue record for this book is available from the British Library

Publisher: Joanna Lorenz
Project Editor: Fiona Eaton
Designer: Bobbie Colgate Stone
Photographers: James Duncan, Michelle Garrett, Nelson Hargreaves, Debbie Patterson
Contributors: Fiona Barnett, Kally Ellis, Tessa Evelegh, Lucinda Ganderton, Ercole Moroni,
Terence Moore, Pamela Westland

Printed and bound in Singapore

Important Addresses

Name ....

Address ....

....

....

Telephone ....

Name ....

Address ....

....

....

Telephone ....

Name ....

Address ....

....

....

Telephone ....

Name ....

Address ....

....

....

Telephone ....

Name ....

Address ....

....

Telephone ....

Name ....

Address ....

....

....

Telephone ....

Name ....

Address ....

....

....

Telephone ....

Name ....

Address ....

....

....

Telephone ....

Name ....

Address ....

....

Telephone ....

Name ....

Address ....

....

....

Telephone ....

Name ....

Address ....

....

....

Telephone ....

Name ....

Address ....

....

....

Telephone ....

Name
Address

Telephone

Name
Address

Telephone

Name
Address

Telephone

These pale-stemmed roses are off-set by the moss and terracotta pot.

A

Gather ye rosebuds while ye
may,
Old Time is still a-flying:
And this same flower that
smiles today
To-morrow will be dying.
Robert Herrick: To the Virgins, to make
much of Time

Name
Address

Telephone

Name
Address

Telephone

Name
Address

Telephone

Name
Address

Telephone

Name
Address

Telephone

Name
Address

Telephone

Name
Address

Telephone

This pretty heart-shaped wreath,
which is made from 40 dried
red rose heads, would make an
unusual and long-lasting
Valentine's Day gift.

_A_

Name
Address

Telephone

Name
Address

Telephone

Name
Address

Telephone

Name
Address

Telephone

Name
Address

Telephone

Name
Address

Telephone

Name
Address

Telephone

Name
Address

Telephone

Name
Address

Telephone

Name
Address

Telephone

Name
Address

Telephone

Name
Address

Telephone

Name
Address

Telephone

Name
Address

Telephone

Apple and lavender make a quirky
topiary tree.

Name ....
Address ....
....

Telephone ....

Name ....
Address ....
....

Telephone ....

Name ....
Address ....
....

Telephone ....

Name ....
Address ....
....

Telephone ....

Name ....
Address ....
....

Telephone ....

Name ....
Address ....
....

Telephone ....

B

Kind words can be short and easy to speak, but their echoes are truly endless.

Mother Theresa

Name ....
Address ....
....

Telephone ....

Name ....
Address ....
....

Telephone ....

Name ....
Address ....
....

Telephone ....

Name ....
Address ....
....

Telephone ....

Name ....
Address ....
....

Telephone ....

Name ....
Address ....
....

Telephone ....

Name ....
Address ....
....

Telephone ....

A pomander of dried rose heads
will give off a gentle aroma.

Name	Name	Name
Address	Address	Address
Telephone	Telephone	Telephone

Name	Name	Name
Address	Address	Name
Telephone	Telephone	Name

Name	Name	Name
Address	Address	Address
Telephone	Telephone	Telephone

This posy is for a special friend, with lavender meaning "devoted attention" and pink roses denoting "affection" or "love" in the language of flowers.

1 Use small bunches of lavender to create the basic structure and shape of the posy.

2 Push single rosebuds into the lavender, spacing them evenly.

3 Edge the posy with wired leaves. Unravel a paper ribbon and use to cover the wire and stalks. Finish off by tying the ends of the ribbon into a bow.

Name

Address

Telephone

Name

Address

Telephone

Name

Address

Telephone

Name

Address

Telephone

Name

Address

Telephone

Name

Address

Telephone

Name

Address

Telephone

Name

Address

Telephone

Dried deep pink peonies and small blue globe thistles are massed tightly around a candle in a terracotta flowerpot, secured in plastic foam for dried flowers.

Name ....
Address ....
....
Telephone ....

Name ....
Address ....
....
Telephone ....

Name ....
Address ....
....
Telephone ....

Name ....
Address ....
....
Telephone ....

Name ....
Address ....
....
Telephone ....

Name ....
Address ....
....
Telephone ....

*Then glut thy sorrow on a
morning rose,
Or on the rainbow of the salt-
sand wave,
Or on the wealth of globed
peonies*

John Keats: Ode on Melancholy

Name ....
Address ....
....
Telephone ....

Name ....
Address ....
....
Telephone ....

Name ....
Address ....
....
Telephone ....

Name ....
Address ....
....
Telephone ....

Name ....
Address ....
....
Telephone ....

Name ....
Address ....
....
Telephone ....

Name ....
Address ....
....
Telephone ....

A still life of scabious and
anemones is most appealing.

C

Name	Name	Name
Address	Address	Address
Telephone	Telephone	Telephone

Name	Name	Name
Address	Address	Address
Telephone	Telephone	Telephone

Name	Name	Name
Address	Address	Address
Telephone	Telephone	Telephone

The soft pastel colours give this trug basket a summery appeal and the starfish evoke images of the sea, making it a delightful bathroom display.

1 Fit a block of plastic foam for dried flowers into a trug basket and create the overall domed shape of the arrangement using 50 natural phalaris stems.

2 Add 40 shell pink rose stems and 20 cream strawflowers, recessing some flowers to give depth. Arrange 100 lavender heads, in groups of five, among the other flowers.

3 Double leg mount 15 small dried starfish on stub (floral) wires and distribute them evenly throughout the display.

Name
Address

Telephone

Name
Address

Telephone

Name
Address

Telephone

Multi-layered tulip heads are
massed in a topiary tree.

D

*If Jove would give the leafy
bowers
A queen for all their world of
flowers
The rose would be the choice
of Jove,
And blush the queen of every
grove*

Sappho

Name
Address

Telephone

Name
Address

Telephone

Name
Address

Telephone

Name
Address

Telephone

Name
Address

Telephone

Name
Address

Telephone

Name
Address

Telephone

Name
Address

Telephone

Roses, eucalyptus and scabious, gathered from the garden, are tied in a simple posy, wrapped in brown paper and finished off with a pretty ribbon bow.

Name ....
Address ....
....
Telephone ....

Name ....
Address ....
....
Telephone ....

Name ....
Address ....
....
Telephone ....

Name ....
Address ....
....
Telephone ....

Name ....
Address ....
....
Telephone ....

Name ....
Address ....
....
Telephone ....

D

Name ....
Address ....
....
Telephone ....

Name ....
Address ....
....
Telephone ....

Name ....
Address ....
....
Telephone ....

Name ....
Address ....
....
Telephone ....

Name ....
Address ....
....
Telephone ....

Mistletoe and winterberry are tied on to a twisted cane ring with twine to make a traditional kissing ring. Checked ribbons are used to hang the finished ring.

Name
Address

Telephone

Name
Address

Telephone

Name
Address

Telephone

Name
Address

Telephone

Name
Address

Telephone

Name
Address

Telephone

E

The holly and the ivy,
When they are both full
grown,
Of all the trees that are in the
wood,
The holly bears the crown.

Anon, 16th century

Name
Address

Telephone

Name
Address

Telephone

Name
Address

Telephone

Name
Address

Telephone

Name
Address

Telephone

Name
Address

Telephone

Name
Address

Telephone

Name
Address

Telephone

Simply mixing three or four types
of foliage can be very effective.

Name ....
Address ....
....
Telephone ....

Name ....
Address ....
....
Telephone ....

An aromatic, culinary topiary is set
in a toning flowerpot.

Name ....
Address ....
....
Telephone ....

Name ....
Address ....
....
Telephone ....

Name ....
Address ....
....
Telephone ....

Name ....
Address ....
....
Telephone ....

Name ....
Address ....
....
Telephone ....

Name ....
Address ....
....
Telephone ....

Name ....
Address ....
....
Telephone ....

Name ....
Address ....
....
Telephone ....

Name ....
Address ....
....
Telephone ....

Name ....
Address ....
....
Telephone ....

Name ....
Address ....
....
Telephone ....

This star-shaped wall decoration
is made of cinnamon sticks and is
embellished with lavender. A
delightful aromatic mix of flowers
and spices will fill the air.

Name ....
Address ....
....
Telephone ....

Name ....
Address ....
....
Telephone ....

Name ....
Address ....
....
Telephone ....

Name ....
Address ....
....
Telephone ....

F

Lavenders blue, dilly dilly
Lavenders green
When I am king, dilly dilly
You shall be queen
Traditional song

Name ....
Address ....
....
Telephone ....

Name ....
Address ....
....
Telephone ....

Name ....
Address ....
....
Telephone ....

Name ....
Address ....
....
Telephone ....

Name ....
Address ....
....
Telephone ....

Name ....
Address ....
....
Telephone ....

Name ....
Address ....
....
Telephone ....

A delicate rose and its own foliage
ensures an elegant corsage.

This romantic pot-pourri is made
of rosebuds, lavender and moss.
Perfume the pot-pourri by
drizzling your favourite essential
oil over the moss.

F

Name	Name	Name
Address	Address	Address
Telephone	Telephone	Telephone

| Name | Name | |
| Address | Address | |

Red roses link these two jewel-like pots visually: contrasting with lime green 'Santini' chrysanthemums in one and combining with purple phlox in the other.

| Telephone | Telephone | |

Wired starfish create a frame for massed shell pink dried rose heads in this beautiful bedroom wreath. Space is left in the design for a hanging ribbon.

Name ....
Address ....
....
Telephone ....

Name ....
Address ....
....
Telephone ....

Name ....
Address ....
....
Telephone ....

Name ....
Address ....
....
Telephone ....

Name ....
Address ....
....
Telephone ....

Name ....
Address ....
....
Telephone ....

Name
Address

Telephone

Name
Address

Telephone

Name
Address

Telephone

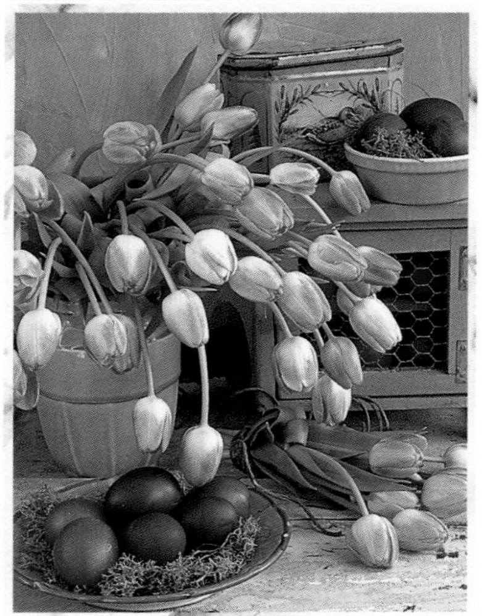

A festive Easter display of tulips and colourful painted eggs.

G

When a friend asks, there is no tomorrow.

17th-century proverb

Name
Address

Telephone

Name
Address

Telephone

Name
Address

Telephone

Name
Address

Telephone

Name
Address

Telephone

Name
Address

Telephone

Name
Address

Telephone

Name
Address

Telephone

Name
Address

Telephone

Name
Address

Telephone

Name
Address

Telephone

Name
Address

Telephone

Name
Address

Telephone

Name
Address

Telephone

Name
Address

Telephone

Name
Address

Telephone

Name
Address

Telephone

Name
Address

Telephone

Name
Address

Telephone

Name
Address

Telephone

Name
Address

Telephone

Name
Address

Telephone

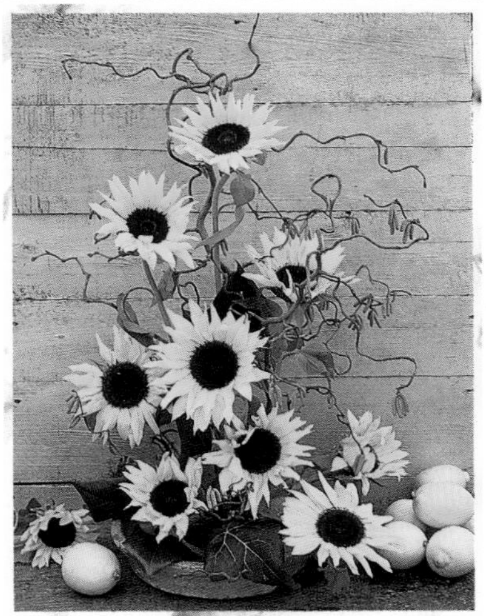

Contorted hazel twigs give support to the bright yellow sunflowers.

Name
Address

Telephone

Name
Address

Telephone

Name
Address

Telephone

Name

Address

Telephone

Name

Address

Telephone

Name

Address

Telephone

Name

Address

Telephone

A fruity tree for the kitchen of
beech leaves and preserved pears.

HI

Then give the world the best
that you have
And the best will come back
to you.

Madeline Bridges

Name

Address

Telephone

Name

Address

Telephone

Name

Address

Telephone

Name

Address

Telephone

Name

Address

Telephone

Name

Address

Telephone

Name

Address

Telephone

Name

Address

Telephone

A change from mistletoe and
holly at Christmas is provided by
this 30 cm (12 in) wreath which
incorporates wired clementines,
pyracanthus and ivy leaves.

Name	Name	Name
Address	Address	Address
Telephone	Telephone	Telephone

Name	Name	Name
Address	Address	Address
Telephone	Telephone	Telephone

Name	Name	Name
Address	Address	Address
Telephone	Telephone	Telephone

This delightful arrangement combining forest fruits and rosehips with garden anemones becomes a sumptuous display when placed in an elegant vase.

1 Fill your chosen vase with water and use blackberry stems to establish the outline shape. Add rosehips to create a visual balance (strip the thorns from the stems first).

2 Add white Japanese anemones (these are 'Honorine Jobert') throughout the arrangement. Take particular care when handling these delicate flowers.

3 Add the vine leaves to the arrangement so that they form a collar around the base of the vase.

JK

Name ....
Address ....
....
Telephone ....

Name ....
Address ....
....
Telephone ....

Name ....
Address ....
....
Telephone ....

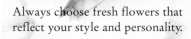

Always choose fresh flowers that
reflect your style and personality.

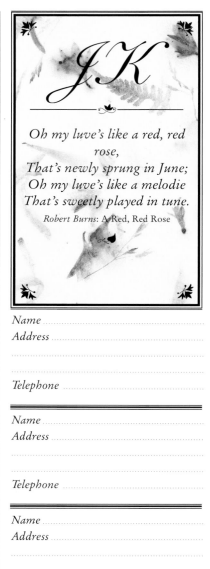

JK

Oh my luve's like a red, red
rose,
That's newly sprung in June;
Oh my luve's like a melodie
That's sweetly played in tune.

Robert Burns: A Red, Red Rose

Name ....
Address ....
....
Telephone ....

Name ....
Address ....
....
Telephone ....

Name ....
Address ....
....
Telephone ....

Name ....
Address ....
....
Telephone ....

Name ....
Address ....
....
Telephone ....

Name ....
Address ....
....
Telephone ....

Name ....
Address ....
....
Telephone ....

Name ....
Address ....
....
Telephone ....

To create these sophisticated napkin decorations, suitable for a wedding reception, wrap an ivy trail around a napkin, then make a hand-spiralled, flat-backed sheaf using four or five lily-of-the-valley stems, and three cyclamen flowers and leaves. Tie with gold cord then position on the ivy and secure in place with the cord.

Name ....
Address ....

....

Telephone ....

Name ....
Address ....

....

Telephone ....

Name ....
Address ....

....

Telephone ....

Name ....
Address ....

....

Telephone ....

JK

Name	*Name*
Address	*Address*
Telephone	*Telephone*

Name	*Name*
Address	*Address*
Telephone	*Telephone*

Name

Address

Telephone

This ring is strongly evocative of the seaside. Mussel shells are glued to the plastic foam ring and globe thistles are pushed into the foam to fill the gaps.

Name ....
Address ....
....
Telephone ....

Name ....
Address ....
....
Telephone ....

Name ....
Address ....
....
Telephone ....

Name ....
Address ....
....
Telephone ....

Name ....
Address ....
....
Telephone ....

Name ....
Address ....
....
Telephone ....

L

Friendships multiply joys and divide griefs.

19th-century proverb

Name ....
Address ....
....
Telephone ....

Name ....
Address ....
....
Telephone ....

Name ....
Address ....
....
Telephone ....

Name ....
Address ....
....
Telephone ....

Name ....
Address ....
....
Telephone ....

Name ....
Address ....
....
Telephone ....

Name ....
Address ....
....
Telephone ....

Name ....
Address ....
....
Telephone ....

Bold shapes and colours give this display a contemporary feel.

L

Classical urns lend dried-flower
arrangements a timeless feel.

Name

Address

Telephone

Name

Address

Telephone

Name

Address

Telephone

Name

Address

Telephone

Name

Address

Telephone

Name

Address

Telephone

Name

Address

Telephone

Name

Address

Telephone

Name

Address

Telephone

Name

Address

Telephone

Name

Address

Telephone

An audacious combination of
orange roses set against vivid
purple anemones and metallic
blue berries of laurustinus makes
a vibrant Christmas display.

M

Name ....
Address ....

....

Telephone ....

Name ....
Address ....

....

Telephone ....

A fresh herbal wreath makes an
ideal gift for an enthusiastic cook.

Name ....
Address ....

....

Telephone ....

Name ....
Address ....

....

Telephone ....

M

The rainbow comes and goes,
And lovely is the rose;
William Wordsworth: Ode Intimations
of Immortality

Name ....
Address ....

....

Telephone ....

Name ....
Address ....

....

Telephone ....

Name ....
Address ....

....

Telephone ....

Name ....
Address ....

....

Telephone ....

Name ....
Address ....

....

Telephone ....

Name ....
Address ....

....

Telephone ....

Name ....
Address ....

....

Telephone ....

This welcoming wreath is made
with pliable buddleia branches.
Trailing ivy and red berries are
entwined around the heart and a
white rose completes the design.

Massed dried flowers never fail to
create an impressive display.

Name

Address

Telephone

Name

Address

Telephone

Name

Address

Telephone

Name

Address

Telephone

Name

Address

Telephone

Name

Address

Telephone

Name

Address

Telephone

Name

Address

Telephone

Name

Address

Telephone

Name

Address

Telephone

Name

Address

Telephone

Name

Address

Telephone

Name

Address

Telephone

Name

Address

Telephone

Name

Address

Telephone

Name

Address

Telephone

Name

Address

Telephone

Name

Address

Telephone

Name

Address

Telephone

Name

Address

Telephone

Name

Address

Telephone

N

Beauty, strength, youth, are
flowers but fading seen;
Duty, faith, love, are roots
and ever green.

George Peel: A Farewell to Arms

Name

Address

Telephone

Name

Address

Telephone

Name

Address

Telephone

Name

Address

Telephone

Name

Address

Telephone

Name

Address

Telephone

Name

Address

Telephone

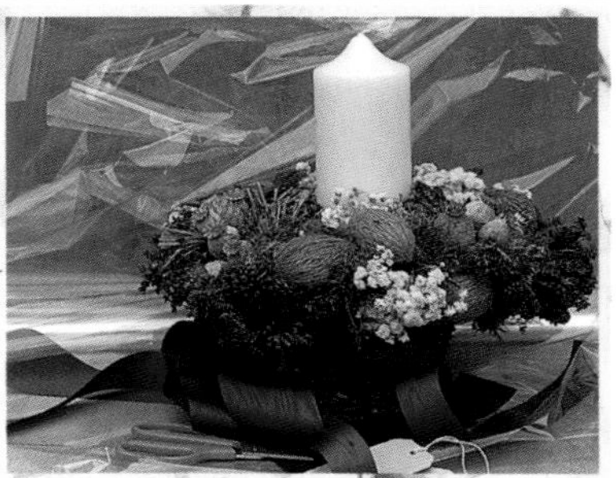

This flower-edged basket with a candle makes a lovely gift.

Name ....
Address ....
....
Telephone ....

Name ....
Address ....
....
Telephone ....

Name ....
Address ....
....
Telephone ....

Name ....
Address ....
....
Telephone ....

Name ....
Address ....
....
Telephone ....

Name ....
Address ....
....
Telephone ....

Name ....
Address ....
....
Telephone ....

Name ....
Address ....
....
Telephone ....

Tussie mussies make perfect gifts or small table centrepieces. One features blackberry stems and Japanese anemones; the other delphiniums and rosehip stems.

These arrangements are ideal for young bridesmaids. The birch leaves, yellow roses and fennel are secured in plastic foam. A raffia bow completes the design.

Name

Address

Telephone

Name

Address

Telephone

Name

Address

Telephone

Name

Address

Telephone

Name

Address

Telephone

Name

Address

Telephone

O

Name
Address

Telephone

Name
Address

Telephone

Name
Address

Telephone

Name
Address

Telephone

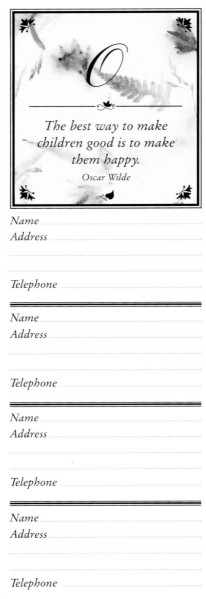

*The best way to make
children good is to make
them happy.*
Oscar Wilde

Name
Address

Telephone

Name
Address

Telephone

Name
Address

Telephone

Name
Address

Telephone

Name
Address

Telephone

Name
Address

Telephone

Name
Address

Telephone

Name
Address

Telephone

Name
Address

Telephone

To straighten stems, wrap them in
newspaper and stand in cool water.

Name ....
Address ....
....
Telephone ....

Name ....
Address ....
....
Telephone ....

Name ....
Address ....
....
Telephone ....

Cheerful pink and yellow
"mini-gerbera", simply pushed
into plastic foam in enamel mugs,
form a naive, colourful group that
children will love.

Name ....
Address ....
....
Telephone ....

Name ....
Address ....
....
Telephone ....

Name
Address

Telephone

Name
Address

Telephone

Name
Address

Telephone

Fabric, flowerpots and dried
flowers make up this pretty swag.

P 2

In the last month of May
I made her posies;
I heard her often say
That she loved roses
Anon: Phillada Flouts Me

Name
Address

Telephone

Name
Address

Telephone

Name
Address

Telephone

Name
Address

Telephone

Name
Address

Telephone

Name
Address

Telephone

Name
Address

Telephone

In Elizabethan times pomanders
were filled with herbs or flowers
and carried to perfume the air.
Today they are more likely to be a
bridesmaid's accessory.

Name	*Name*	*Name*
Address	*Address*	*Address*
Telephone	*Telephone*	*Telephone*
Name	*Name*	*Name*
Address	*Address*	*Address*
Telephone	*Telephone*	*Telephone*
Name	*Name*	*Name*
Address	*Address*	*Address*
Telephone	*Telephone*	*Telephone*

This delicate arrangement in a practical container is an ideal gift for parents on the birth of a baby.

1 Wedge some soaked plastic foam into a small, galvanized bucket and use a bunch of *Pittosporum* to create the domed outline.

2 Distribute 15 pale pink tulips (these are 'Angelique') throughout the foliage then add five stems of white spray roses, with buds at the outside and full blooms in the centre.

3 Add 10 stems each of white ranunculus and phlox and finally add lavender, in groups of three, evenly throughout the flowers and foliage. Tie a patterned ribbon around the bucket and finish in a generous bow.

R

Name

Address

Telephone

Name

Address

Telephone

Name

Address

Telephone

Larkspur, roses and hydrangea are tiered in a round basket.

It is astonishing how short a time it takes for wonderful things to happen.

Frances Hodgson Burnett

Name

Address

Telephone

Name

Address

Telephone

Name

Address

Telephone

Name

Address

Telephone

Name

Address

Telephone

Name

Address

Telephone

Name

Address

Telephone

Name

Address

Telephone

Name

Address

Telephone

Tiered baskets are very effective and one of the easiest displays for a beginner. For a dramatic display, ensure that each layer of flowers is the correct height.

Name ....
Address ....
....
Telephone ....

Name ....
Address ....
....
Telephone ....

A collection of these delightful dried-flower pew ends produces a dramatic effect in church. The candle is taped between two canes and dried pink larkspur and roses conceal the fixing. The flowers are secured with stub (floral) wires and tied with a large raffia bow. A strong S-shaped wire is attached to the back for hanging.

Name
Address

Telephone

Name
Address

Telephone

Name
Address

Telephone

Name
Address

Telephone

Name
Address

Telephone

Name
Address

Telephone

S

*Came the Spring with all its
splendour,
All its birds and all its
blossoms
All its flowers, and leaves and
grasses*

Henry Wadsworth Longfellow: The Song
of Hiawatha

Name
Address

Telephone

Name
Address

Telephone

Name
Address

Telephone

Name
Address

Telephone

Name
Address

Telephone

Name
Address

Telephone

Name
Address

Telephone

A cinnamon covered Advent candle
burns down to Christmas.

Nuts and fir cones combine in a
garland trimmed with a bow.

Name
Address

Telephone

Name
Address

Telephone

Name
Address

Telephone

Name
Address

Telephone

Name
Address

Telephone

Name
Address

Telephone

Name
Address

Telephone

Name
Address

Telephone

Name
Address

Telephone

Name
Address

Telephone

Name
Address

Telephone

An old picture frame is used as
the base of this love-and-kisses
collage. Crossed cinnamon sticks
make the "kisses" while tropical
seedheads are the hearts.

T

Name

Address

Telephone

Name

Address

Telephone

Name

Address

Telephone

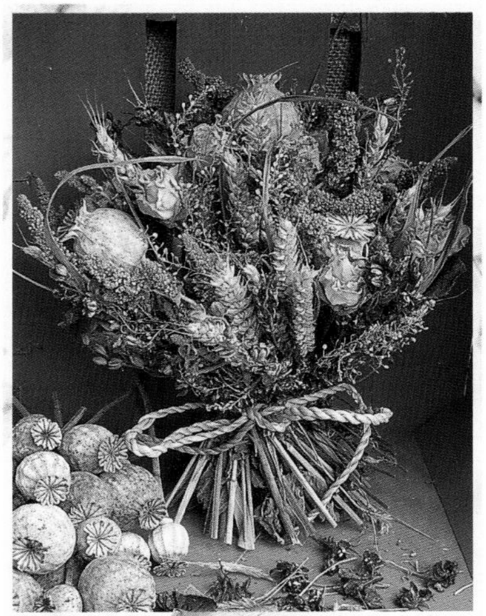

A flower stack brings welcome
warmth and colour to a room.

T

*Friends tie their purses with a
cobweb thread.*

19th-century proverb

Name

Address

Telephone

Name

Address

Telephone

Name

Address

Telephone

Name

Address

Telephone

Name

Address

Telephone

Name

Address

Telephone

Name

Address

Telephone

Name

Address

Telephone

Name

Address

Telephone

Name
Address

Telephone

Name
Address

Telephone

Name
Address

Telephone

Name
Address

Telephone

Name
Address

Telephone

The bright reds, yellows and green on the olive oil tin make it an attractive container for this arrangement of 40 dried 'Jacaranda' roses.

Name	Name	Name
Address	Address	Address
Telephone	Telephone	Telephone

Name	Name	Name
Address	Address	Address
Telephone	Telephone	Telephone

Name	Name	Name
Address	Address	Address
Telephone	Telephone	Telephone

This wreath will fill any room with the rich scent of summer lavender.

1 Tie a length of natural rope to a 30 cm (12 in) diameter twig wreath.

2 Hold a bunch of lavender across the wreath with the flowers pointing outwards. Wind the rope around the stems, then over the wreath, and spiral bind the stems in place.

3 Place a second lavender bunch to the right of the first; bind in place. Continue to spiral bind bunches until the wreath is covered. Tie off the rope securely and finish off with a loop for hanging.

Name

Address

Telephone

Name

Address

Telephone

Name

Address

Telephone

Name

Address

Telephone

Grouping displays of simple
flowers can increase their impact.

U V W

Come in the evening, or come
in the morning
Come when you're looked for,
or come without warning

Thomas Davis: The Welcome

Name

Address

Telephone

Name

Address

Telephone

Name

Address

Telephone

Name

Address

Telephone

Name

Address

Telephone

Name

Address

Telephone

Name

Address

Telephone

Name

Address

Telephone

Name

Address

Telephone

Golden pompon dahlias have
long, straight stems which makes
them easy to arrange in a large
display. Here they are supported
by campanula and rosehips.

U V W

Name
Address

Telephone

Name
Address

Telephone

Name
Address

Telephone

Pressed flowers make lovely personalized greetings cards.

Name
Address

Telephone

Name
Address

Telephone

Name
Address

Telephone

Name
Address

Telephone

Name
Address

Telephone

Name
Address

Telephone

Name
Address

Telephone

Name
Address

Telephone

Name
Address

Telephone

Name
Address

Telephone

Personalize a gift to a special friend by using handmade paper scattered with pressed flowers. Secure with twine and tuck three dried red roses underneath.

Name ....
Address ....
....
Telephone ....

Name ....
Address ....
....
Telephone ....

Name ....
Address ....
....
Telephone ....

XYZ

*The red rose cries, 'She is near, she is near'
And the white rose weeps, 'She is late';
The larkspur listens, 'I hear, I hear'
And the lily whispers, 'I wait'.*

Alfred, Lord Tennyson: Maud

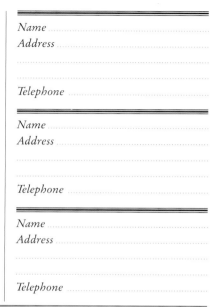

Name ....
Address ....
....
Telephone ....

Name ....
Address ....
....
Telephone ....

Name ....
Address ....
....
Telephone ....

This simple fireplace display should be turned occasionally when in situ so that it fades evenly.

1 Put some scrunched-up chicken wire in the basket. You will need one bunch each of amaranthus, pink larkspur, pink roses, red roses and lavender for the design.

2 Push individual stems of amaranthus through the wire mesh to the bottom of the basket. Add stems of larkspur, distributing them evenly.

3 Add the roses and lavender, placing some rose heads low down for added interest. Check that the balance of the design is correct from all angles.

XYZ

Name	Name	Name
Address	Address	Address
Telephone	Telephone	Telephone

Name	Name	Name
Address	Address	Address
Telephone	Telephone	Telephone

Name	Name	Pale pink roses and peonies give a summery, soft look to this fire-place arrangement and the logs and raffia bow give the display a countryside feel.
Address	Address	
Telephone	Telephone